ALI BABA
AND THE *FORTY THIEVES*

ALI BABA
AND THE FORTY THIEVES

RETOLD BY **MATTHEW K. MANNING**
ILLUSTRATED BY **RICARDO OSNAYA**

DESIGNER: **BRANN GARVEY**
EDITOR: **DONALD LEMKE**
ASSOC. EDITOR: **SEAN TULIEN**

ART DIRECTOR: **BOB LENTZ**
CREATIVE DIRECTOR: **HEATHER KINDSETH**
EDITORIAL DIRECTOR: **MICHAEL DAHL**

Raintree is an imprint of Capstone Global Library Limited, a company incorporated in England and Wales having its registered office at 7 Pilgrim Street, London, EC4V 6LB – Registered company number: 6695582

To contact Raintree:
Phone: 0845 6044371
Fax: + 44 (0) 1865 312263
Email: myorders@raintreepublishers.co.uk
Outside the UK please telephone +44 1865 312262.

Text © Stone Arch Books 2011
First published in the United Kingdom by Capstone Global Library in 2013
The moral rights of the proprietor have been asserted.

ISBN 978 1 406 26186 8 (paperback)
17 16 15 14 13 12
10 9 8 7 6 5 4 3 2 1

British Library Cataloguing in Publication Data
A full catalogue record for this book is available from the British Library.

CONTENTS

CAST OF CHARACTERS

KASIM

ALI BABA

ALI BABA'S WIFE

MARJANA

ALI BABA'S SON

THE CAPTAIN ...
AND HIS 39 THIEVES

If we're spotted, the firewood will be the least of your worries!

Faster! Faster!

CLOP!
CLOP!
CLOP!
CLOP!
CLOP!

Here they come.

Now stay still . . .

. . . or they're sure to find us!

21

24

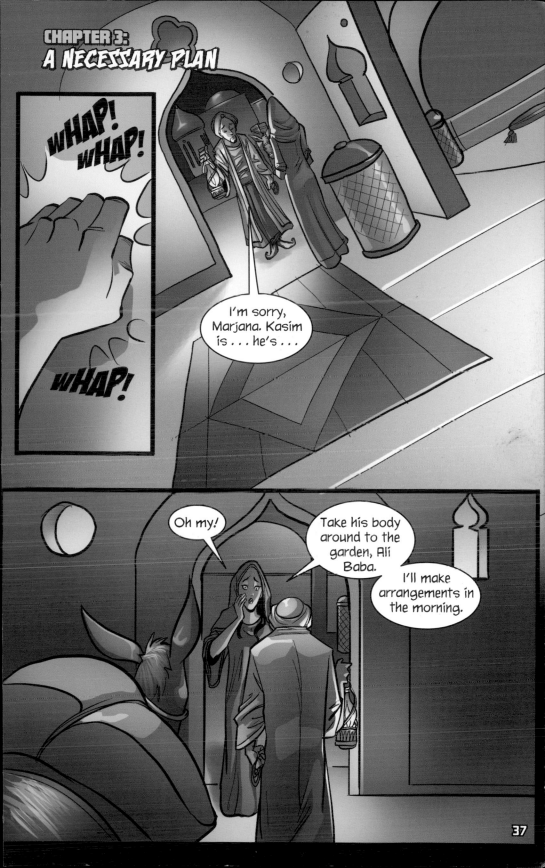

41

42

I'm glad you're all moving in here.

I was getting lonely without Kasim.

Yes, I think it's for the best.

Is that everything, Marjana?

Yes, Ali Baba. Thank you.

I just hope Father feels the same.

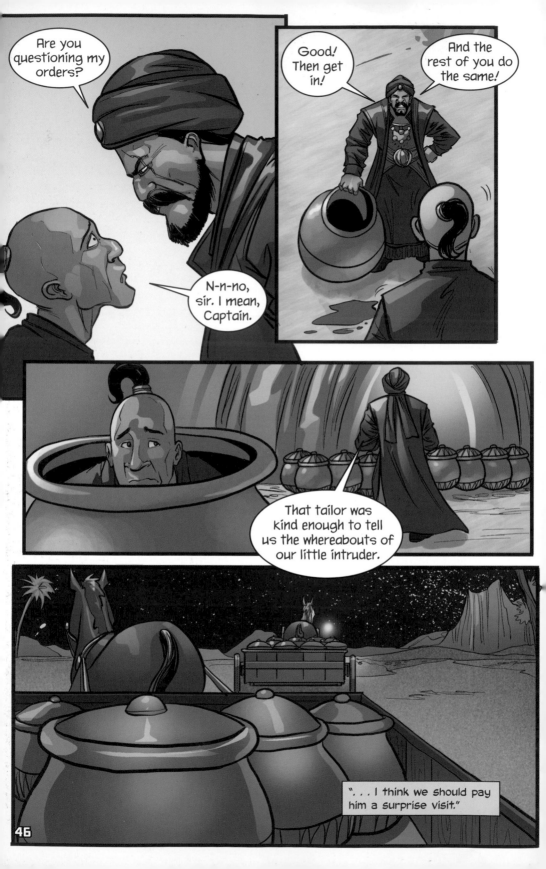

No, my son. This gift carries much more weight.

What is it, Father?

A simple phrase . . .

"Open sesame."

ARABIAN NIGHTS

The story of "Ali Baba and the Forty Thieves" is part of a collection of Middle Eastern and South Asian folktales known as *One Thousand and One Nights.* These tales have been passed down from generation to generation for hundreds of years. The first English-language edition, entitled *The Arabian Nights' Entertainment,* was published in 1706.

Since then, many versions of the book have been published – some containing more than 1,000 stories. In each of these editions, the tales of mystery and adventure are told by the same narrator, a beautiful woman named Scheherazade. She has just married an evil ruler who plans to kill her before the night is through. To stop him, Scheherazade entertains the king with a new story each night, and he soon forgets about his deadly plan.

The Arabian Nights tales remain some of the greatest stories ever told. They include popular adventures, such as "The Fisherman and the Genie", "The Seven Voyages of Sinbad", and "Ali Baba and the Forty Thieves". Many of these stories have been adapted into films, books, and plays that are still popular today.

REAL HIDDEN TREASURES

In 1520, Spanish explorer Hernando Cortes and his men raided the Aztec empire, stealing the treasure of their emperor, Montezuma. Before the Spanish crew could escape, the Aztecs attacked, and the jewels were spilled and buried around Lake Tezcuco, near modern day Mexico City. Despite many efforts, these treasures have never been found.

Edward Thatch, the pirate known as Blackbeard, plundered the high seas in the early 1700s, stealing gold and other riches. He died in 1718, but his treasure was never found. Many still believe it's hidden somewhere in the Caribbean Sea.

In 1922, archeologist Howard Carter found the tomb of Egyptian pharaoh Tutankhamen, also known as King Tut, which was filled with millions of pounds worth of gold and jewels. However, many believe other tombs remain hidden, waiting to be discovered.

ABOUT THE AUTHOR

Matthew K. Manning is a comic book writer, historian, and fan. Over the course of his career, he's written comics or books starring Batman, Superman, Iron Man, Wolverine, Spider-Man, the Incredible Hulk, the Legion of Super-Heroes, the Justice League, and even Bugs Bunny. Some of his more recent works include DK Publishing's *Marvel Chronicle* and Running Press's *The Batman Vault*. He is currently writing a mini-series for the DC Comics imprint Wildstorm. He lives in Brooklyn, New York, with his wife Dorothy and has a baby girl on the way.

ABOUT THE ILLUSTRATOR

Ricardo Osnaya is a self-taught illustrator, living and working in Mexico. Since first publishing editorial illustrations in *Excelsior Magazine*, Osnaya has made a name for himself as a freelance artist. He's published the comics *Burundis* and *Dos Guerreros* and illustrated popular characters, such as the Power Rangers. Currently, Osnaya collaborates with Protobunker Studio and works as a comic and illustration instructor at the Mexican Institute of Youth and other schools.

GLOSSARY

arrangement plans for something to happen, such as a funeral service

basin large bowl used for washing

cargo goods carried by some form of transport, such as a mule

cavern large cave

courtyard open area surrounded by walls

curiosity desire to know something

gruesome disgusting or horrible

inform tell someone something

intruder person who forces their way into a place where they are not wanted

secure safe, firmly closed, or well protected

sesame small oval seed that comes from a tropical plant

stubborn difficult to deal with

tailor someone who makes or alters clothes

DISCUSSION QUESTIONS

1. Ali Baba stole from the thieves because he needed money for his family. Do you think stealing is ever right? Explain your answer.

2. Marjana kills the evil captain. She believes this action is the only way to protect herself and her family. Do you think her decision was okay? Why or why not?

3. At the end of the story, Ali Baba tells his son the secret password to the treasure cave. Do you think Ali Baba's son will use the password to get more riches? Explain.

WRITING PROMPTS

1. Write a final chapter to this book. What happens next? Does Ali Baba's son go back to the cave? Do the authorities ever find out about the missing thieves? You decide.

2. If you had a cave full of treasure, what would you buy? Write a story describing how you would use the riches.

3. Imagine your own Arabian Nights tale. Think of a story filled with mystery and adventure. Then write it down and read it to friends and family.

ARABIAN NIGHTS TALES

ALADDIN AND THE MAGIC LAMP

The legendary tale of Aladdin, a poor youth living in the city of Al Kal'as. One day, the crafty boy outsmarts an evil sorcerer, getting his hands on a magical lamp that houses a wish-fulfilling genie! Soon, all of Aladdin's dreams come true, and he finds himself married to a beautiful princess. All is well until, one day, the evil sorcerer returns to reclaim the lamp.

ALI BABA AND THE FORTY THIEVES

The legendary tale of Ali Baba, a young Persian boy who discovers a cave filled with gold and jewels, the hidden treasures of 40 deadly thieves. Unfortunately, his greedy brother, Kasim, cannot wait to get his hands on the riches. Returning to the cave, he is captured by the thieves and killed, and now the evil men want revenge on Ali Baba as well.